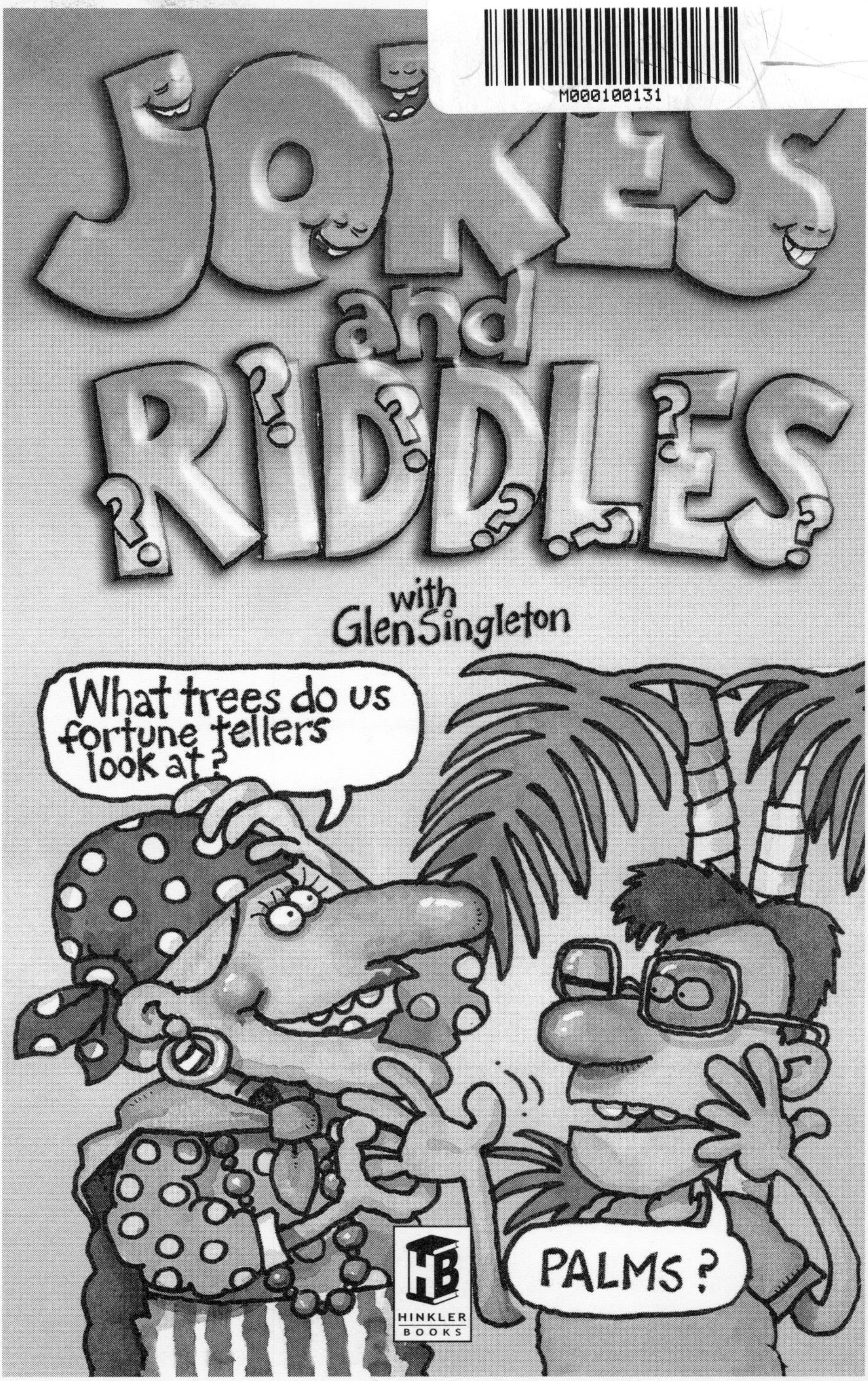
JOKES
and
RIDDLES
with
Glen Singleton
What trees do us fortune tellers look at?
PALMS?
HB
HINKLER
BOOKS

Cover Illustration & Illustrations: Glen Singleton
Cover Design: Hinkler Books Studio

Jokes and Riddles
Published in 2004 by Hinkler Books Pty Ltd
17–23 Redwood Drive
Dingley VIC 3172 Australia
www.hinklerbooks.com

Reprinted 2004

ISBN: 1 7412 1746 6
Printed and bound in Australia

Jokes and Riddles

with Glen Singleton

What are two things you cannot have for breakfast?

Lunch and dinner.

What has eyes that cannot see, a tongue that cannot taste, and a soul that cannot die?

A shoe.

What can you hear but not see and only speaks when it is spoken to?

An echo.

How many apples can you put in an empty box?

One. After that it's not empty anymore.

When will water stop flowing downhill?

When it reaches the bottom.

What's easier to give than receive?

Criticism.

What's red and goes up and down?

A tomato in an elevator.

Why do firemen wear red braces?

To keep their trousers up.

When do clocks die?

When their time's up.

What kind of dress can never be worn?

Your address.

What word is always spelt incorrectly?

Incorrectly.

What has a bottom at the top?

A leg.

What's an ig?

An Eskimo's house without a toilet.

What's the last thing you take off before bed?

Your feet off the floor.

What is always coming but never arrives?

Tomorrow.

What can you serve but never eat?

A volleyball.

What do you put in a barrel to make it lighter?

A hole.

What stays in the corner and travels all around the world?

A postage stamp.

Who was the fastest runner in the whole world?

Adam, because he was the first in the human race.

How does a fireplace feel?

Grate!

What gets wet the more you dry?

A towel.

What's green, has eight legs and would kill you if it fell on you from out of a tree?

A billiard table.

What breaks when you say it?

Silence.

What bow can't be tied?

A rainbow.

Why are false teeth like stars?

They come out at night.

What goes all around a pasture
but never moves?

A fence.

Why did the boy throw butter out the window?

Because he wanted to see a butterfly!

What is H204?

Drinking.

What can you hold without touching?

Your breath.

What goes up the chimney down, but not down the chimney up?

An umbrella.

What is big, red, and eats rocks?

A big red rock eater.

What goes all over the world but doesn't move?

The highway.

What starts with a P, ends with an E, and has a million letters in it?

Post Office.

What is always behind the times?

The back of a watch.

Why can't it rain for two days in a row?

Because there is a night in between.

What is the fiercest flower in the garden?

The tiger lily.

What goes up and down but never moves?

A flight of stairs.

How many seconds are there in a year?

twelve . . . 2nd of January, 2nd of February . . .

Which candle burns longer, a red one or a green one?

Neither, they both burn shorter.

Which is the longest rope?

Europe.

What runs but doesn't get anywhere?

A refrigerator.

What can be caught, heard but never seen?

A remark.

What kind of ship never sinks?

Friendship.

What cup can you never drink out of?

A hiccup.

What kind of star wears sunglasse

A movie star.

What belongs to you but is used more by other people?

Your name.

What kind of cup can't hold water?

A cupcake.

When things go wrong what
can you always count on?

Your fingers.

What can you give away but also keep?

A cold.

What bet can never be won?

The alphabet.

What has two hands, no fingers,
stands still and goes?

A clock.

What is the beginning of eternity, the end of time, the beginning of every ending?

The letter 'E'.

What can't walk but can run?

A river.

What is there more of the less you see?

Darkness.

How can you double your money?

Look at it in the mirror.

What part of a fish weighs the most?

The scales.

What's grey and can't see
well from either end?

A donkey with its eyes shut.

What is bigger when it's upside down?

The number 6.

Why don't bananas get lonely?

Because they hang around in bunches.

What's the difference between
a joke and a wise-guy?

One is funny, and one thinks he's funny.

If a woman is born in China, grows up in Australia, goes to live in America and dies in New Orleans, what is she?

Dead.

What has a hundred limbs but cannot walk?

A tree.

Why did the boy sit on his watch?

He wanted to be on time.

How can you tell an undertaker?

By his grave manner.

If a horse loses its tail, where could it get another?

At a re-tail store.

What goes through water but doesn't get wet?

A ray of light.

What do elephants play marbles with?

Old bowling balls.

Why do doctors wear masks when operating?

Because if they make a mistake, no one will know who did it!

Why is a bride always out of luck on her wedding day?

Because she never marries the best man.

When Adam introduced himself to Eve, what three words did he use which read the same, backward and forward?

'Madam, I'm Adam.'

Why is a ladies' belt like a garbage truck?

Because it goes around and around, and gathers the waist.

When is a chair like a woman's dress?

When it's satin.

What is the difference between a hungry person and a greedy person?

One longs to eat, and the other eats too long.

On what nuts can pictures hang?

Walnuts.

What did the dentist say to the golfer?

'You've got a hole in one!'

When a boy falls into the water, what is the first thing he does?

Gets wet.

What happened when the Eskimo girl had a fight with her boyfriend?

She gave him the cold shoulder.

What do you call someone who doesn't have all their fingers on one hand?

Normal. You have fingers on both hands.

Why did the girl tear the calendar?

Because she wanted to take a month off.

What did Cinderella say when her photos didn't arrive?

'Some day my prints will come.'

Why did the Invisible Man's wife understand him so well?

Because she could see right through him.

Why can't anyone stay angry with actors?

Because they always make up.

Why did the boy laugh after his operation?

Because the doctor put him in stitches.

If everyone bought a white car, what would we have?

A white carnation.

What is a forum?

One-um plus three-um.

What did the burglar say to the lady who caught him stealing her silver?

'I'm at your service, ma'am.'

Why didn't the boy go to work
in the wool factory?

Because he was too young to dye.

Why did the boy put his bed
in the fireplace?

So he could sleep like a log.

When does a timid girl turn to stone?

When she becomes a little bolder (boulder)!

What ten letter word starts with gas?

A-U-T-O-M-O-B-I-L-E.

What did Santa Claus's wife say during a thunderstorm?

'Come and look at the rain, dear.'

Why are good intentions like people who faint?

They need carrying out.

Why were the boy's photos not ready when he called for them?

The photographer was a late developer.

'Do these stairs take you to the third floor?'

'No, I'm afraid you'll have to walk!'

What did the mother shrimp say to her baby when they saw a submarine?

'Don't be scared – it's only a can of people.'

Why is an island like the letter T?

Because it's in the middle of water.

Why do we dress baby girls in pink and baby boys in blue?

Because babies can't dress themselves.

What is higher without the head, than with it?

A pillow.

What kind of song can you sing in the car?

A cartoon (car tune)!

How does a boat show its affection?

By hugging the shore.

What did the buffalo say to his son, when he went away on a long trip?

'Bison.'

What do you draw without
a pencil or paper?

A window shade.

Who gets the sack every
time he goes to work?

The postman.

Why was number 10 scared?

Because 7 8 9 (seven ate nine).

What has no legs but can walk?

A pair of shoes.

What is a prickly pear?

Two hedgehogs.

What runs down the street but has no legs?

The kerb.

Why was the mother flea so sad?

Because her children were going to the dogs.

Which word if pronounced right is wrong
and if pronounced wrong is right?

Wrong.

How do you make a pair of trousers last?

Make the coat first.

What goes around the house and in the house but never touches the house?

The sun.

What is round and deep but could not be filled up by all the water in the world?

A colander.

The more you take, the more
you leave behind. What am I?

Footsteps.

What is put on a table and
cut but never eaten?

A pack of cards.

What trees do fortune-tellers look at?

Palms.

What is the longest word in the world?

Smiles, because there is a mile between the beginning and the end.

What has eyes but cannot see?

A potato.

What starts working only when it's fired?

A rocket.

What is at the end of the world?

The letter 'D'.

What burns longer, a 10 centimetre candle or a 20 centimetre candle?

Neither, they both burn shorter.

What happened to the horse that swallowed the dollar coin?

He bucked.

What can you hold but never touch?

A conversation.

What did Tennessee?

The same thing Arkansas.

What's the centre of gravity?

The letter 'V'.

What clothes does a house wear?

Address.

Where does Friday come before Wednesday?

In the dictionary.

What do you call a man who shaves fifteen times a day?

A barber.

If a butcher is two metres tall and has size eleven feet, what does he weigh?

Meat.

What's black when clean and
white when dirty?

A blackboard.

Does a death adder die if it
bites its own tongue?

Can a snail have houseguests?

If a seven-11 is open 24 hours a day, 365 days
a year, why are there locks on the doors?

If olive oil is made from olives and peanut oil is made from peanuts, what is baby oil made from?

Is it easier to break the long jump world record in a leap year?

If nothing ever sticks to Teflon, how does Teflon stick to the pan?

Do they sterilise needles for lethal injections?

What was the best thing before sliced bread?

What does a girl look for,
but hopes she'll never find?

A hole in her pantyhose.

Where can you always find a helping hand?

At the end of your arm.

What weighs more, a kilo of lead
or a kilo of feathers?

They both weigh the same.

Why is milk the fastest thing in the world?

Because it's pasteurised before you see it.

What sort of ring is always square?

A boxing ring.

What's taken before you get it?

Your picture.

What starts with an 'e', ends with an 'e' and only has one letter in it?

An envelope!

What did the piece of wood say to the drill?

You bore me.

Which room has no door, no windows, no floor and no roof?

A mushroom.

What washes up on very small beaches?

Microwaves.

What gets bigger and bigger as you take more away from it?

A hole.

Why do you go to bed?

Because the bed will not come to you.

What has teeth but cannot eat?

A comb.

What goes up and does not come down?

Your age.

What question can you never answer yes to?

Are you asleep?

What is the only true cure for dandruff?

Baldness.

What was the highest mountain before Mt Everest was discovered?

Mt Everest.

What runs across the floor without legs?

Water.

What has holes and holds water?

A sponge.

What puzzles make you angry?

Crossword puzzles.

What has four fingers and
a thumb but is not a hand?

A glove.

What flies around all day but never goes anywhere?

A flag.

What kind of coat can you put on only when it's wet?

A coat of paint.

What weapon was most feared by medieval knights?

A can-opener.

Where were potatoes first found?

In the ground.

How long should a person's legs be?

Long enough to reach their feet.

When is it bad luck to be
followed by a big black cat?

When you are a little grey mouse.

What dance do hippies hate?

A square dance.

Why did the girl keep a ruler
on her newspaper?

Because she wanted to get the story straight.

Why did the girl buy a set of tools?

Everyone said she had a screw loose.

What do well-behaved young lambs say to their mothers?

'Thank ewe!'

What can you serve, but never eat?

A tennis ball.

Three men were in a boat. It capsized but only two got their hair wet. Why?

The third man was bald!

What's the difference between
an oak tree and a tight shoe?

One makes acorns, the other makes corns ache.

What did one angel say to the other angel?

'Halo.'

What did the egg say to the whisk?

'I know when I'm beaten.'

What does every girl have that she can always count on?

Fingers.

What do you get if you cross a cowboy with a stew?

Hopalong Casserole.

What do you call a ship that lies on the bottom of the ocean and shakes?

A nervous wreck.

How do you make a hotdog stand?

Steal its chair.

Why was Thomas Edison able to invent the light bulb?

Because he was very bright.

What's the best way to win a race?

Run faster than everyone else.

During which battle was Lord Nelson killed?

His last one.

What was more useful than the invention of the first telephone?

The second telephone.

What did one tomato say to the other that was behind?

'Ketchup!'

What's small, annoying and really ugly?

I don't know but it comes when I call my sister's name.

What side of an apple is the left side?

The side that hasn't been eaten.

What invention allows you to see through walls?

A window.

What are the four letters the dentist says when a patient visits him?

ICDK (I see decay).

What's another word for tears?

Glumdrops.

Which months have 28 days?

All of them.

What's green, covered in custard and sad?

Apple grumble.

How do you make a fire with two sticks?

Make sure one of them is a match.

What did the little light bulb say to its mum?

'I wuv you watts and watts.'

Where was Solomon's temple?

On his head.

What fly has laryngitis?

A horsefly (hoarse fly).

What did one wall say to the other wall?

'I'll meet you at the corner.'

Why was the maths book sad?

Because it had too many problems.

What's the letter that ends everything?

The letter 'G'.

What did the stamp say to the envelope?

'Stick with me and we will go places.'

I have ten legs, twenty arms and fifty-four feet. What am I?

A liar.

What did the tie say to the hat?

'You go on ahead, I'll just hang around.'

Who is scared of wolves and swears?

Little Rude Riding Hood.

What did the pencil sharpener
say to the pencil?

'Stop going in circles and get to the point!'

What do Alexander the Great and
Kermit the Frog have in common?

The same middle name!

There are three kinds of people in the world.

Those who can count. And those who can't.

Where do you find giant snails?

At the ends of their fingers.

Name three inventions that have helped man up in the world.

The elevator, the ladder and the alarm clock.

How do you saw the sea in half?

With a sea-saw.

What's the difference between a night-watchman and a butcher?

One stays awake and the other weighs a steak!

What's easy to get into but hard to get out of?

Trouble.

What has many rings but no fingers?

A telephone.

What do you get if you jump into the Red Sea?

Wet.

What do you call a lazy toy?

An inaction figure.

How do you make holy water?

You burn the hell out of it.

What do all the Smiths in the
phone book have in common?

They all have phones.

Why did the bacteria cross the microscope?

To get to the other slide.

What did the little mountain
say to the big mountain?

'Hi Cliff!'

Why did the traffic light turn red?

You would too if you had to change in the middle of the street!

What do bees do if they want to catch public transport?

Wait at a buzz stop.

What is the difference between a jeweller and a jailer?

A jeweller sells watches and a jailer watches cells.

What did one rain drop say to the other?

'Two's company, three's a cloud.'

What did the penny say to the other penny?

We make perfect cents.

What did the Pacific Ocean say to the Atlantic Ocean?

Nothing. It just waved.

Who was the smallest man in the world?

The guard who fell asleep on his watch.

What can jump higher than a house?

Anything, houses can't jump!

What sort of star is dangerous?

A shooting star.

Which of the witch's friends eats the fastest?

The goblin.

Why did the balloon burst?

Because it saw a lolly pop.

Why did the farmer plough his field with a steamroller?

He wanted to grow mashed potatoes.

What's the difference between an elephant and a matterbaby?

What's a matterbaby?

Nothing, but thanks for asking!

What did the shirt say to the blue jeans?

'Meet you on the clothesline—that's where I hang out!'

What did the big hand of the clock say to the little hand?

'Got a minute?'

What kind of music does your father like to sing?

Pop music.

What's the easiest way to find a pin in your carpet?

Walk around in your bare feet.

What did the parents say to their son who wanted to play drums?

'Beat it!'

What's the difference between
Santa Claus and a warm dog?

Santa wears the suit, but a dog just pants.

Where do you find baby soldiers?

In the infantry.

Can February March?

No. But April May.

What's the definition of intense?

That's where campers sleep.

What do you call a man who stands around and makes faces all day?

A clockmaker.

Did you hear the one about the man who went into the cloning shop?

When he came out he was beside himself!

What did the key say to the glue?

'You wanna be in show biz kid? Stick to me, I can open up doors for you!'

When does B come after U?

When you take some of its honey.

What did the didgerido?

Answered the phone when the boomerang.

Where are the Andes?

At the end of your armies.

Where does a sick ship go?

To the dock.

Did I tell you the joke about the high wall?

I'd better not, you might not get over it.

What did the first mind reader say to the second mind reader?

'You're all right, how am I?'

What did one ear say to the other ear?

'Between you and me we need a haircut.'

What flowers grow under your nose?

Tulips.

What did the ear 'ear.

Only the nose knows.

Did you know that Davey Crockett had three ears?

A right ear, a left ear and a wild frontier.

Why was the glow-worm unhappy?

Her children weren't very bright.

Why does the ocean roar?

You would too if you had
crabs on your bottom.

What will go up a drainpipe down
but won't go down a drainpipe up?

An umbrella.

What would you call superman
if he lost all his powers?

Man.

What has a hundred legs but can't walk?

Fifty pairs of pants.

What are the names of the small rivers that run into the Nile?

The juve-niles.

What do you know about the Dead Sea?

Dead? I didn't even know it was sick!

Where is the English Channel?

Not sure – it's not on my TV.

Name an animal that lives in Lapland.

A reindeer.

Now name another.

Another reindeer.

What fur do we get from a tiger?

As fur as possible.

Statistics say that one in three people is mentally ill.

So check your friends and if two of them seem okay, you're the one . . .

What birds are found in Portugal?

Portu-geese.

Name three famous poles.

North, south and tad.

How do you make a potato puff?

Chase it around the garden.

What jam can't you eat?

A traffic jam.

If the Mounties always get their man, what do postmen always get?

Their mail.

Why are giraffes good friends to have?

Because they stick their neck out for you.

What do you get if you cross a worm with a baby goat?

A dirty kid.

What's the hottest letter in the alphabet?

It's 'b', because it makes oil boil!

What do you get when you cross an orange with a squash court?

Orange squash.

What's green and short and
goes camping?

A boy sprout.

We went for a holiday last year
to a seaside town.

It was so boring there that the tide went out one day and didn't come back!

What happened when there was a
fight in the fish and chip shop?

Two fish got battered.

What's the difference between a young lady and a fresh loaf?

One is a well-bred maid and the other is well-made bread.

What did the big chimney say to the little chimney?

'You're too young to smoke.'

What did the big telephone say to the little telephone?

'You're too young to get engaged.'

What did the power point say to the plug?

'Socket to me.'

What has four wheels and flies?

A garbage truck.

What helps keep your teeth together?

Toothpaste.

What is red and white?

Pink.

How do fishermen make a net?

They make lots of holes and tie them together with string.

What time do most people go to the dentist?

Tooth-hurty.

What's small and wobbly and sits in a pram?

A jelly baby.

Why do artists make lots of money?

Because they can draw their own wages.

When do mathematicians die?

When their number is up.

What is the difference between
a bus driver and a cold?

*One knows the stops, the
other stops the nose.*

What did the ground say to the rain?

'If this keeps up, I'll be mud.'

What vegetable goes well with jacket potatoes?

Button mushrooms.

Who steals from her grandma's house?

Littler Red Robin Hood.

What colour is a hiccup?

Burple.

Why was the broom late?

It overswept.

How do Eskimos dress?

As quickly as possible.

How do you make a Maltese cross?

Hit him on the head.

How much does Uluru (Ayers Rock) weigh?

One stone.

What's purple, 5000 years old and 400 kilometres long?

The Grape Wall of China.

When is a car not a car?

When it has turned into a driveway.

What do you do with crude oil?

Teach it some manners.

Why did the car get a puncture?

There was a fork in the road.

What do you call a man with a bus on his head?

Dead.

How many animals did
Moses fit in the Ark?

None, it was Noah's Ark.

How did Noah steer the Ark at night?

He switched on the floodlights.

Where was Noah when the
lights went out?

In d'ark.

What did Noah say as he was loading the animals?

'Now I herd everything.'

How do we know that Moses was sick?

God gave him tablets.

How did the Vikings send messages?

By Norse code.

Do you know where to find elephants?

Elephants don't need finding – they're so big they don't get lost.

Where are English kings and queens crowned?

On the head.

Where's Hadrian's Wall?

Around his garden.

Who invented the weekend?

Robinson Crusoe – he had all his work done by Friday.

Who is the smelliest person in the world?

King Pong.

What do traffic wardens put on their sandwiches?

Traffic jam.

Did you hear about the criminal contortionist?

He turned himself in.

Why was the baby pen crying?

Because its mum was doing a long sentence.

Did you hear about the unlucky sailor?

First he was shipwrecked, then he was rescued – by the Titanic.

Can a match box?

No but a tin can.

Why are gloves clumsy?

Because they're all fingers and thumbs.

Why did the snowman dress up?

Because he was going to the snowball.

What happened when the bell fell in the swimming pool?

It got wringing wet.

Why did the gangster kill his pet pig?

Because it squealed to the police.

How did the comedian pass the time in hospital?

By telling sick jokes.

Why did the criminals whisper in the meadow?

Because they didn't want to be overheard by the grass.

When is a car like a frog?

When it is being toad.

Twenty puppies were stolen from a pet shop. Police are warning people to look out for anyone selling hot dogs.

Why does the Statue of Liberty stand in New York harbour?

Because it can't sit down.

What is green and pecks on trees?

Woody Wood Pickle.

What wears an anorak and pecks on trees?

Woody Wood Parka.

What did the waterfall say to the fountain?

'You're just a little squirt.'

Who's faster than a speeding bullet and full of food?

Super Market.

Who delivers Christmas presents to the wrong houses?

Santa Flaws.

Which song is top of the Eskimo hit parade?

'There's No Business Like Snow Business.'

What wears nine gloves, eighteen shoes and a mask?

A baseball team.

How do you get four suits for a couple of dollars?

Buy a pack of cards.

Why is the Mississippi such an unusual river?

It has four eyes and can't even see.

What did one elevator say to the other?

'I think I'm coming down with something.'

What did one magnet say
to the other magnet?

'I find you very attractive.'

What did the rug say to the floor?

'Don't move, I've got you covered.'

How do prisoners call home?

On cell phones.

Why do bagpipers walk
when they play?

*They're trying to get
away from the noise.*

What's Chinese and deadly?

Chop sueycide.

Why is it impossible to die of
starvation in the desert?

*Because of the sand which is there
(sandwiches there).*

What did the dentist want?

The tooth, the whole tooth and nothing but the tooth.

Why did the belt go to jail?

Because it held up a pair of pants.

Police have arrested two kids, one for playing with fireworks, and one for stealing a battery. They charged one and let the other one off.

Who were the world's shortest lovers?

Gnomeo and Juliet.

What do you get when
two prams collide?

A creche.

What are government workers
called in Spain?

Seville servants.

How do you make antifreeze?

Lock her outside in the cold.

What did the shoe say to the foot?

'You're having me on.'

Who swings through the cakeshop, yodelling?

Tarzipan.

What did one sole say to the other?

'I think we're being followed by a couple of heels.'

Why did E.T. have such big eyes?

Because he saw his phone bill.

What were the gangster's final words?

'What is that violin doing in my violin case?'

What's the definition of minimum?

A very small mother.

What illness do retired pilots get?

Flu.

When is a door not a door?

When it is ajar.

Where do old Volkswagens go?

To the old volks home.

Which trees are always sad?

Pine trees.

When is the cheapest time to phone friends?

When they're not home.

How do you clean the sky?

With a skyscraper.

Why did the bungy jumper
take a vacation?

Because he was at the end of his rope.

Who was the father of the Black Prince?

Old King Coal.

Why did the Mexican push
his wife over the cliff?

Tequila.

What did the electrician's wife
say when he got home?

'Wire you insulate.'

Which bus could sail the oceans?

Columbus.

Why did Henry VIII have so many wives?

He liked to chop and change.

What did the hat say to the scarf?

'You hang around and I'll go ahead.'

When does the alphabet
only have 24 letters?

When U and I aren't there.

Why are rivers lazy?

Because they never get off their beds.

What do you call a snowman with a suntan?

A puddle.

Did Adam and Eve have a date?

No, they had an apple.

Where did Captain Cook stand when he landed in Australia?

On his feet.

How do you use an Egyptian doorbell?

Toot-and-come-in.

How can you tell a dogwood tree?

By its bark.

Where does Tarzan buy his clothes?

At a jungle sale.

Why did Polly put the kettle on?

She didn't have anything else to wear.

Why do toadstools grow so close together?

They don't need mushroom.

Where did the king keep his armies?

Up his sleevies.

What do you call a boomerang
that doesn't come back to you?

A stick.

Where was the Declaration of Independence signed?

At the bottom.

Why does lightning shock people?

It doesn't know how to conduct itself.

What's the easiest way to get on TV?

Sit on it.

What has four legs and doesn't walk?

A table.

What's brown, hairy and
has no legs but walks?

Dad's socks.

'Mum, why isn't my nose
twelve inches long?'

'Because then it would be a foot.'

How did the rocket lose his job?

He was fired.

What's yellow and wears a mask?

The Lone Banana.

What do you get if you cross the Atlantic with the Titanic?

About half way.

What's the difference between a TV and a newspaper?

Ever tried swatting a fly with a TV?

How much does it cost for
a pirate to get earrings?

A buccaneer!

What did the digital clock
say to its mother?

'Look ma, no hands.'

What do hippies do?

They hold your leggies on.

How did the octopus couple walk down the road?

Arm in arm, in arm, in arm, in arm, in arm, in arm, in arm, in arm . . .

What do snakes write on the bottom of their letters?

With love and hisses!

Witch: 'When I'm old and ugly, will you still love me?'

Wizard: 'I do, don't I?'

What happened when the young wizard met the young witch?

It was love at first fright.

Did you hear about the vampire who died of a broken heart?

She had loved in vein.

Why did the girl separate the thread from the needle?

Because the needle had something in its eye.

Why did the girl wear a wet shirt all day?

Because the label said 'wash and wear'.

What do you call an amorous insect?

The love bug!

Why did the boy spend two weeks in a revolving door?

Because he was looking for the doorknob.

Did you hear about the girl who wrote herself a letter, but forgot to sign it?

When it arrived, she didn't know who it was from!

Brother: 'What happened to you?'

Sister: 'I fell off while I was riding.'

Brother: 'Horseback?'

Sister: 'I don't know. I'll find out when I get back to the stable.'

First Girl: 'Why are you putting your horse's saddle on backwards?'

Second Girl: 'How do you know which way I'm going?'

Why did the girl cut a hole
in her new umbrella?

*Because she wanted to tell when
it stopped raining.*

Why doesn't your sister like peanuts?

Have you ever seen a skinny elephant?

What kind of sharks never eat women?

Man-eating sharks!

Why did the boy feed money to his cow?

Because he wanted to get rich milk.

Why did the boy tiptoe past the medicine cabinet?

Because he didn't want to wake the sleeping pills.

My sister went on a crash diet.

Is that why she looks a wreck?

Why did the girl give cough syrup to the pony?

Because someone told her it was a little horse.

Why didn't the person want tickets for a door prize?

Because they already had a door.

Why did the girl have yeast and shoe polish for breakfast?

Because she wanted to rise and shine in the morning!

What does every winner lose in a race?

Their breath.

Why is a scrambled egg like the English cricket team?

They both get beaten.

What are the four seasons?

Baseball, basketball, soccer, and football!

What has 22 legs and two wings
but can't fly?

A soccer team.

What is the smelliest sport?

Ping Pong!

What race is never won?

A swimming race.

Why was the boxer known as Picasso?

Because he spent all his time on the canvas.

What did one bowling ball say to the other?

'Don't stop me I'm on a roll.'

Why did the runner wear
rippled sole shoes?

To give the ants a fifty-fifty chance.

What happens when cricketers get old?

They go batty.

Why were the arrows nervous?

Because they were all in a quiver.

What's a ghost's favourite
position in soccer?

Ghoul-keeper.

What do you get when you cross
a footballer with a gorilla?

*I don't know but nobody tries
to stop it from scoring.*

Why did all the bowling pins go down?

Because they were on strike.

What illness do martial artists get?

Kung Flu.

Why do soccer players have
so much trouble eating?

They think they can't use their hands.

Why was the centipede two hours
late for the soccer match?

It took him two hours to put his shoes on.

Why are cricket players always so cool?

Because of all the fans.

Why was the chickens' soccer match a bad idea?

Because there were too many fowls.

Why is tennis such a noisy game?

Because everyone raises a racket.

Why is Cinderella so bad at sport?

Because she has a pumpkin for a coach and she runs away from the ball.

Why did the golfer wear two sets of pants?

In case he got a whole in one.

What job does Dracula have with the Transylvanian baseball team?

He looks after the bats.

What do you call a cat that plays football?

Puss in boots.

When is a baby like a basketball player?

When he dribbles

'I can't see us ever finishing this ten-pin bowling game.'

'Why is that?'

'Every time I knock all the pins down, someone calls everyone out on strike!'

What part of a football ground smells the best?

The scenter spot!

Why aren't football stadiums built in outer-space?

Because there is no atmosphere!

Which goalkeeper can jump higher than a crossbar?

All of them – a crossbar can't jump!

Why did the footballer hold his boot to his ear?

Because he liked sole music.

Where do footballers dance?

At a football.

What are Brazillian soccer fans called?

Brazil nuts.

Why did a footballer take a piece of rope onto the pitch?

He was the skipper.

What lights up a football stadium?

A football game.

If you have a referee in football, what do you have in bowls?

Cornflakes.

What is a goal keeper's favourite snack?

Beans on post.

How do hens encourage their football teams?

They egg them on.

Who won the race between two balls of string?

They were tied.

How did the basketball court get wet?

The players dribbled all over it.

Why don't grasshoppers go to football matches?

They prefer cricket matches.

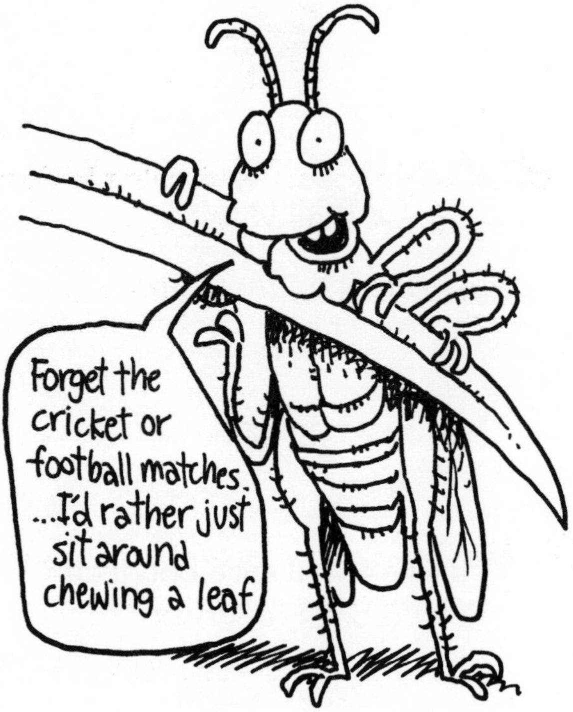

Why didn't the dog want to play football?

It was a boxer.

When fish play football, who is the captain?

The team's kipper.

How do you stop squirrels playing football in the garden?

Hide the ball, it drives them nuts!

Why should you be careful when playing against a team of big cats?

They might be cheetahs.

Why do football coaches bring suitcases along to away games?

So that they can pack the defence.

Name a tennis player's favourite city.

Volley Wood.

Why was the struggling manager seen shaking the club cat?

To see if there was any money in the kitty.

Where do football directors go when they are sick of the game?

The bored room.

Coach: 'Our new player cost ten million. I call him our wonder player.'

Fan: 'Why's that?'

Coach: 'Every time he plays, I wonder why I bothered to buy him!'

Coach: 'I thought I told you to lose weight. What happened to your three week diet?'

Player: 'I finished it in three days!'

Coach: 'I'll give you $100 a week to start with, and $500 a week in a year's time.'

Young player: 'See you in a year!'

What did the football player say when he accidentally burped during the game?

'Sorry, it was a freak hic!'

What part of a basketball stadium is never the same?

The changing rooms.

Where do old bowling balls end up?

In the gutter.

Why do artists never win when
they play basketball?

They keep drawing.

What did they call Dracula
when he won the premiership?

The Champire.

Why does someone who runs marathons
make a good student?

Because education pays off in the long run.

What is a runner's favourite subject in school?

Jog-raphy.

What stories are told by basketball players?

Tall stories.

Why was the computer so tired when it got home?

Because it had a hard-drive.

Where are computers kept at school?

On their floppy desks.

How many programmers does it take to screw in a light bulb?

None, it's a hardware problem.

Where do you find the biggest spider?

In the world wide web.

What do you get if you cross a computer programmer with an athlete?

A floppy diskus thrower.

Hey, did you see who stole my computer?

'Yes he went data way!'

What did the computer say to the programmer at lunchtime?

'Can I have a byte?'

What do computers do when they get hungry?

They eat chips.

'Is that the computer help line? Every time I log on to the Seven Dwarves website, my computer screen goes snow white.'

How do computers make sweaters?

On the interknit.

Why was the computer so thin?

Because it hadn't had many bytes.

What sits in the middle of
the world wide web?

A very, very big spider.

Why did the vampire bite a computer?

Because he wanted to get on the interneck.

Customer: 'I cleaned my computer and now it doesn't work.'

Repairman: 'What did you clean it with?'

Customer: 'Soap and water.'

Repairman: 'Water's never meant to get near a computer!'

Customer: 'Oh, I bet it wasn't the water that caused the problem . . . it was when I put it in the spin dryer!'

Did you hear about the monkey who left bits of his lunch all over the computer?

His dad went bananas.

'Do you turn on your computer with your left hand or your right hand?'

'My right hand.'

'Amazing! Most people have to use the on/off switch!'

How do you stop your laptop batteries from running out?

Hide their sneakers.

'I bought this computer yesterday and I found a twig in the disk drive!'

'I'm sorry Sir, you'll have to speak to the branch manager.'

'I've been on my computer all night!'

'Don't you think you'd be more comfortable on a bed, like everyone else?'

'Mum, Mum, Dad's broken my computer!'

'How did he do that?'

'I dropped in on his head!'

What did the computer say when a man typed something in on the keyboard?

'You're really pushing my buttons, little man!'

Why did the computer cross the road?

Because it was programmed by the chicken.

Why did the computer sneeze?

It had a virus.

What is the computer's favourite dance?

Disk-o.

Why was the computer in pain?

It had a slipped disk!

Why did the cat sit on the computer?

To keep an eye on the mouse.

Teacher: 'I hope I didn't see you copying from John's exam paper, James.'

James: 'I hope you didn't see me either!'

Father: 'How do you like going to school?'

Son: 'The going bit is fine; the coming home bit too – it's the bit in the middle I don't like!'

Did you hear about the student who said he couldn't write an essay on goldfish for his homework, because he didn't have any waterproof ink?

Have you heard about the gym teacher who ran around exam rooms, hoping to jog students' memories?

. . . Or, the craft teacher who had her pupils in stitches?

. . . Or, the cookery teacher who thought Hamlet was an omelette with bacon?

. . . Or, the maths teacher who wanted to order pizza for dinner, but was divided about whether to have additional cheese?

'Our teacher talks to herself in class, does yours?'

'Yes, but she doesn't realise it. She thinks we're listening!'

'Be sure to go straight home from school.'

'I can't – I live around the corner!'

. . . Or, the technology teacher who left teaching to try to make something of himself?

Mother: 'I told you not to eat cake before supper.'

Son: 'But it's part of my homework – see – If you take an eighth of a cake from a whole cake, how much is left?'

Teacher: 'What came after the Stone Age and the Bronze Age?'

Student: 'The saus-age.'

Did you hear about the cross-eyed teacher?

He couldn't control his pupils.

Teacher: 'What's the name of a liquid that won't freeze?'

Student: 'Hot water.'

Teacher: 'Can anyone tell me what the Dog Star is?'

Student: 'Lassie.'

Mother: 'Did you get a good place in the geography test?'

Daughter: 'Yes, I sat next to the cleverest kid in the class.'

'Of course, in my day we didn't have computers at school to help us . . .

We got our schoolwork wrong all on our own!'

Dad: 'How did you find your maths exam?'

Son: 'Unfortunately, it wasn't lost!'

Why did the student stand on his head?

To turn things over in his mind.

Why did the teacher wear sunglasses?

Because his students were so bright.

What do you get if you cross a teacher and a traffic warden?

Someone who gives you 500 double yellow lines for being late.

What is an English teacher's favourite fruit?

The Grapes of Wrath.

What is the easiest way to
get a day off school?

Wait until Saturday.

How many letters are there in the alphabet?

Eleven. Count them -t-h-e-a-l-p-h-a-b-e-t!

Why can you believe everything a
bearded teacher tells you?

They can't tell bare-faced lies.

Teacher: 'Why can't you answer any of my questions in class?'

Student: 'If I could, there wouldn't be much point in me being here.

How does a maths teacher know how long she sleeps?

She takes a ruler to bed.

Playing truant from school is like having a credit card.

Lots of fun now, pay later.

Why was the head teacher worried?

Because there were so many rulers in the school.

Did you hear about the teacher who locked the school band in a deep freeze?

They wanted to play really cool jazz.

Why did the boy throw his watch out of the window during an exam?

Because he wanted to make time fly.

Teacher: 'What family does the octopus belong to?'

Student: 'Nobody's I know.'

Ben's teacher thinks Ben is a wonder child.

She wonders whether he'll ever learn anything.

Teacher: 'Are you good at arithmetic?'

Mary: 'Well, yes and no.'

Teacher: 'What do you mean, yes and no?'

Mary: 'Yes, I'm no good at arithmetic.'

Teacher: 'Your daughter's only five and she can spell her name backwards! Why, that's remarkable!'

Mother: 'Yes, we're very proud of her.'

Teacher: 'And what is your daughter's name?'

Mother: 'Anna.'

'What are three words most often used by students?' the teacher asked the class.

'I don't know,' sighed a student.

'That's correct!' said the teacher.

Shane: 'Dad, today my teacher yelled at me for something I didn't do.'

Dad: 'What did he yell at you for?'

Shane: 'For not doing my homework.'

'Dad, can you write in the dark?'

'I suppose so.'

'Good. Can you sign my report card, please?'

'Dad, I's been expelled.'

'What? We spend a fortune on sending you to an exclusive private school and you still say "I's".'

'Mum, why do I have to go to school? The kids all make fun of me and all the teachers hate me.'

'Because you're the headmaster, son.'

Geography teacher: 'What's the coldest country in the world?'

Student: 'Chile.'

Teacher: 'If I bought one hundred buns for a dollar, what would each bun be?'

Student: 'Stale.'

English teacher: 'Spell Mississippi.'

Student: 'The river or the state?'

English teacher: 'Jamie, give me a sentence beginning with "I".'

Jamie: "I" is . . .'

Teacher: 'No Jamie, you must always say "I am".'

Jamie: 'Okay. "I" am the ninth letter of the alphabet.'

History teacher: 'Here is a question to check that you did your homework on British kings and queens. Who came after Mary?'

Student: 'Her little lamb.'

History teacher: 'What was Camelot?'

Student: 'A place where camels are parked.'

History teacher: 'What's a Grecian Urn?'

Student: 'About $500 a week.'

What would you get if you crossed
a teacher with a vampire?

Lots of blood tests.

History teacher: 'What's the best thing about history?'

Mary: 'All the dates.'

History teacher: 'Why do we refer to the period around 1000 years AD as the Dark Ages?'

Student: 'Because there were so many knights.'

Maths teacher: 'Paul. If you had five pieces of chocolate and Sam asked for one of them, how many would you have left?'

Paul: 'Five.'

Never go to school on an empty stomach. Go on the bus instead.

Principal: 'You should have been here at 9.00 o'clock.'

Student: 'Why, what happened?'

In which class do you learn how to shop for bargains?

Buy-ology.

Science teacher: 'What are nitrates?'

Student: 'Cheaper than day rates.'

Teacher: 'I wish you'd pay a little attention.'

Student: 'I'm paying as little attention as possible.'

Student: 'Would you punish someone for something they didn't do?'

Teacher: 'Of course not.'

Student: 'Good, because I didn't do my homework.'

Laugh, and the class laughs with you.

But you get detention alone.

Science teacher: 'Which travels faster, heat or cold?'

Student: 'Heat, because you can catch a cold.'

Student to teacher: 'I don't want to worry you but my dad said that if my grades don't improve, someone's going to get a spanking.'

What's the difference between a train station and a teacher?

One minds the train, the other trains the mind.

Teacher: 'Jane, why did you miss school yesterday?'

Jane: 'I didn't miss it at all.'

Teacher: 'That's three times I've asked you a question. Why won't you reply?'

'Because you told me not to answer you back.'

Why are maths teachers good at solving detective stories?

Because they know when all the clues add up.

What is the robot teacher's favourite part of the day?

Assembly.

Did you hear about the two history teachers who were dating?

They go to restaurants to talk about old times.

Did you hear about the teacher who wore sunglasses to give out exam results?

He took a dim view of his students' performance.

What type of instruments did the early Britons play?

The Anglo-saxophone.

What kind of tests do witch teachers give?

Hex-aminations.

Simple Simon was writing a geography essay for his teacher. It began like this:

The people who live in Paris are called parasites . . .